MANTU
the
ELEPHANT

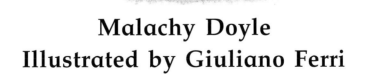

Malachy Doyle
Illustrated by Giuliano Ferri

RIGBY

Chapter 1

Mantu was born under the wide open sky.
His mother stroked him with her trunk.
Mantu was her first baby.
  The other elephants all came to stroke Mantu.
Then his mother helped him onto his legs,
and fed him.

3

Mantu grew fast. The sun was strong and the land grew dry. Every day, the elephants marched across the hot, dusty land. Every day, they had to march further and further to find food and water. Mantu held onto his mother's tail with his trunk.

4

One day the sun was **very** strong.

"I'm so thirsty!" Mantu cried.

"Don't worry," said his mother. "We'll find water.
Kim, the wise old elephant, knows where to go."

At last the elephants came to water.

Little Mantu was thirsty. He was so happy to see the cool, clear water that he ran to the river.

He was about to jump in, but his mother chased after him and held him tightly by the tail.

Kim, the oldest elephant, always went in first to look for crocodiles.

"The water is safe," Kim cried.

8

The elephants began to drink and play in the evening light.

Mantu's mother filled up her trunk and drank the clear cool water.

"I want to do that," thought Mantu.

Then the elephants got washed. They filled their trunks with water and sprayed their dusty backs.

"Wow!" thought Mantu. "I want to do that."

But Mantu couldn't use his trunk yet. He was still too young. He could fill his trunk with water, but it fell out before he could drink it.

He had to put his head under the water to drink. He wished he could use his trunk like a **big** elephant.

11

Mantu's mother sprayed his back.
Mantu tried to spray his mother but
he couldn't. The water all fell out of his
trunk back into the river.

Little Mantu was sad and a little angry. He wanted to learn how to spray with his trunk.

"You have to practise," said his mother.

"I will!" cried Mantu.

Chapter 2

After a while, the elephants went back to the riverbank, and rolled in the mud.

Mantu's mother called to him, but Mantu stayed in the water. He was trying to fill his trunk.

Suddenly, Kim **ROARED**. The other elephants looked up to see what was wrong. A crocodile had slipped into the river and was swimming toward Mantu.

Mantu was in **terrible danger!**

Mantu didn't see the crocodile,
and he didn't hear Kim roaring.
He was learning how to use his trunk.

The crocodile was getting closer and closer to Mantu. Kim **ROARED** again, as loud as she could, and Mantu looked up. He saw the crocodile swimming towards him. He tried to get to the bank, but his feet were stuck in the mud. He cried with fear.

Mantu's mother ran to him. She held onto his tail, and pulled as hard as she could. But Mantu's legs were still stuck in the mud.

Mantu was very, very scared. He knew that crocodiles attack baby elephants.

Kim saw that Mantu was stuck. She saw the crocodile getting closer to him. She roared again and ran to the river. She filled up her trunk, and sprayed the crocodile with water.

The other elephants all ran into the river too. They all sprayed the crocodile.

Then Kim lifted the crocodile up with her tusks. It thrashed its tail in anger. Kim tossed the crocodile high in the air.

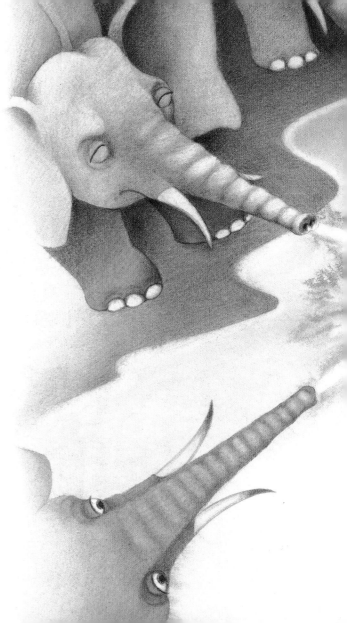

It fell to the water with a loud **SPLASH**
and swam away.

The other elephants pushed and pulled little Mantu. Finally, with one sharp tug, they got him out of the mud.

Mantu stood on the bank, trembling. His mother began to stroke him, but he was still shaking.

Mantu still had some water in his trunk. Suddenly, he sprayed the water all over his mother. Mantu was amazed when the water flew out of his trunk!

"Well done, Mantu," said his mother.

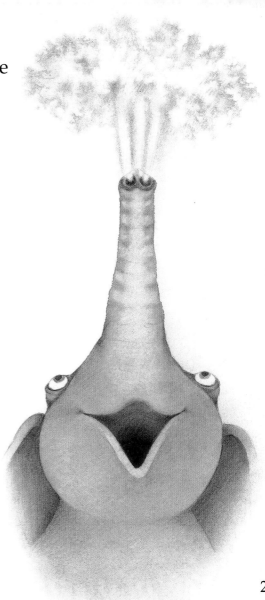

Mantu couldn't believe his luck! He was safe from the crocodile, and he had learned to use his trunk properly.

"At last I'm like all the other elephants," he said.